LUTON I

Nicola Quinn

Life Without Panic Attacks
by Nicola Quinn
Paperback ISBN 1 873483 95 3

First Edition Published 2005
Second Edition Published September 2008

Published by:
DragonRising Publishing
The StarFields Network
45 Gildredge Road
Eastbourne
BN21 4RY
United Kingdom

Web: http://DragonRising.com
Tel: +44 (0)1323 700 123

Printed and bound by CPI Antony Rowe, Eastbourne

To my father

Table of Contents

Introduction

I have known Nicola Quinn for many years, not just as an outstanding holistic practitioner and teacher but also as a personal friend. As such, I was well aware of her struggle to overcome a problem from an older time which left its echoes and daily disturbances in the here-and-now.

I have been present during her brave journey to reclaim her life, her creativity and her abilities to contribute to others. This book is not just an instruction manual, a sensible self help guide and an inspiration to others who suffer from anxiety and panic attacks, but also immensely practical because she has really been there and has triumphed over the fears that were trying to hold her back.

Her personal and practically useful approaches and step-by-step instructions on what to do arc born out of personal experience, and that is invaluable.

I sincerely wish and hope that others who have had their lives limited by panic attacks and paid the terrible cost of self esteem and self actualisation take this book to heart and allow Nicola to guide them, to inspire them, day by day, to do the treatments and find out for themselves how small triumphs build one after the other, until we emerge on the other side, free and clear.

"Life Without Panic Attacks" is a wonderful, heartfelt aid, guide and inspiration, full of integrity and good common sense, gentle, supportive, but most of all, practical and workable - a true light at the end of the dark tunnel of fear.

This is a book that will help many.

Silvia Hartmann PhD

- *Director, Association For Meridian Energy Therapies*
- *Author "Adventures In EFT", "The Advanced Patterns of EFT"*

Foreword

In this wonderful book, Nicola Quinn describes how new discoveries about the human energy system enable rapid, easy and gentle recovery from anxiety states and other emotional problems. She tells her own inspiring story of how she herself recovered from panic attacks using these methods.

Many people experience panic attacks and phobic anxieties at certain periods of life. These are really very common – and can be extremely disabling and distressing. Often the sufferer will conceal the extent of the problem because of feelings of shame. Effective help is not always easily available. Counselling and other purely talk-based therapies are unlikely to resolve the problem. Drugs may only mask the symptoms.

Many forms of cognitive and behavioural therapy aim to persuade the person gradually to face the situations that evoke terror, and try to help him or her to think more rationally – but this is often simply too difficult for the person in the grip of a phobia, who may end up feeling even worse when the therapy fails. The problem with conventional forms of treatment is that they are not easily able to remove the basic reaction of anxiety.

This is where Emotional Freedom Techniques (EFT), EmoTrance, and other forms of energy therapy can help. By tapping on the energy system, using similar principles to those of acupressure, it is possible to release the anxieties and other troubling emotions very easily and quickly, and without great distress.

Nicola Quinn describes very clearly and in detail how to use EFT to address the various aspects of phobias and anxieties. The secret of using the method effectively is in knowing what issues to target when tapping – and Nicola states all of these explicitly.

Panic attacks and anxiety states often arise when a person has been experiencing a period of prolonged or severe stress, so that the mind and body are overwhelmed. He or she may struggle on, trying to cope, not recognising the extent of the strain. Suddenly there is the experience of panic, a terror of collapse and a sense of being unable to go on.

This state of overwhelming terror is in itself a further trauma. The sufferer may fear that he or she is going mad. What then may happen is that the person becomes afraid of a repeat of the panic – and so the cycle of 'fear of fear' sets in.

Another factor is that when people are anxious they may hyperventilate, taking too much oxygen into the blood, resulting in various alarming physical sensations – further adding to the spiralling anxiety. Once the fear of fear is established it tends to fuel itself and intensify over time, since every flicker of anxiety will evoke the fear of panic, thus generating more anxiety. A method is required that can break into this vicious cycle of anxiety – and EFT is exactly that.

Nicola Quinn's book provides both encouragement and a real solution to the sufferer from panic and anxiety. EFT is supported by very good research and is now used by some doctors and other practitioners within the NHS. However, Nicola knows these problems from her own experience – and her recovery is a magnificent testimony to the effectiveness of the methods she describes.

Phil Mollon PhD

- *Psychotherapist and Consultant Clinical Psychologist*
- *Head of Psychology and Psychotherapy Services, Lister Hospital, Stevenage*
- *Author of "EMDR and the Energy Therapies – Psychoanalytic Perspectives"*

Welcome to Life Without Panic Attacks!

This is the book I so desperately looked for when I started having panic attacks, long before the days of the internet and when you still went down to your local library to look for information, and there was nothing. I couldn't believe it and am so happy now that I have written what I needed then and even happier because I know it works!

This book began as an article 'Panic Attacks and EFT' which I wrote after a friend had been to my website and couldn't find anything on the subject even though he knew it was energy therapies that had finally cured me.

As it contains many of the key points, let us begin there with an overview of how I first cured myself of panic attacks with this extraordinary technique.

How I Cured Myself of Panic Attacks

Looking back, when my panic attacks started I was going through some very stressful changes in my life although at the time nothing out of the ordinary seemed to be happening and the attacks just seemed to be getting in the way of my normal living. I would have given anything to have a pill or something to take to stop my heart palpitating (and I did take the drug you could quite easily buy over the counter to try and keep my stomach relaxed) but nothing helped and the more anxious I got about experiencing them the more frequently they occurred.

Nowhere To Turn

It was all very frightening at a time when panic attacks were not generally recognized and I really did think at one point I was going mad and I didn't even have the support of the doctor I was then registered with who just kept checking my blood pressure and declaring me in perfect health.

I knew I was sick but all I could do was protect myself by limiting my experiences to reduce the likelihood of the attacks. This was manageable and worked quite well until eight years on, when my daughter was 4 and I started having them inside my own home when I was on my own with her, and it was then I really began to pull my hair out.

After that it would go in cycles, just beginning to feel ok again and wham, another series would hit, seemingly out of the blue and set me back to square one again, it was all very depressing and no matter how much I read, how ever many remedies I took or however much I meditated I was never ready for the shock of how they made me feel.

Discovering EFT

So when I first met Silvia Hartmann, at an Animal MBS event in 1996 she had organized, and was introduced to Adventures in EFT she had just written, I wasn't overly optimistic but simply set about reading yet another book that was supposedly going to set me free.

But by god, after the first few minutes reading I knew this was something different and moments later, having tried the protocol, my overall anxiety levels were down to zero, something only an hour or two of meditation had previously achieved.

I started off, as I think many people do, with a rather too general statement, Even though I am feeling anxious... but the results of that one round of tapping were enough to prove to me how effective it was and I went on to refine my statements.

The real breakthrough occurred when I started listening to my own body, started concentrating on my feelings, it was then I got the right Opening Statements.

Tapping On Physical Sensations

I first concentrated on the bodily sensations which scared me because I feared they heralded a panic attack.

The description of the physical symptoms became the Opening Statements:

- **Even though when my heart flutters I am scared I will get a full blown attack...**
- **Even though I am scared when my throat gets dry and tight...**
- **Even though getting dizzy when I am out really scares me...**
- **Even though needing to go to the toilet urgently when I am out freaks me out...**
- **Even when things suddenly go loud...**
- **Even when everything goes bright...**

I then decided to imagine it was time to go out and felt the well known feeling of tightness around my chest which I used to get when I bent down to put my shoes on, so instantly dealt with the tightness, I remember it taking two rounds but got it down to zero before carrying on.

Thinking About Doing It...

I then imagined putting my coat on, approaching the front door, tapping all the time, just gently on each point one at a time as the pictures of what I was doing were going through my mind and when anything hit me particularly badly I stopped and concentrated on that. Actually opening the door was the next big problem so I did a few rounds of:

- **Even though the thought of opening the front door is making me feel sick...**

until it was down to zero and then I opened the door in my mind and walked down my path. I waited at the gate and looked around, slight anxiety arose but I tapped it down and walked around the block.

I remember when I got almost exactly half way round feeling a tightness again and tapped for:

- **Even though I am half way and once I take another step I am committed to going on and can't turn back...**

Well I did complete the journey in my head right down to taking my coat and shoes off and sitting back down in my chair in my study and was also quite surprised to feel the customary feeling of relief and achievement which was encouraging.

Going Out

So there was nothing else for it but to actually do it myself, I put on my coat and shoes, felt a little tightness in my throat which turned out to be 'suppose none of this works while I am out?' so I did a round of:

- **Even though I don't believe this is going to work…**

…until it reached zero then opened the door, and proceeded to walk around the block.

I didn't rush but took my time, looking at the front gardens, breathing in the scent of the flowers, noticing where the sun was in the sky and thinking how beautiful the sunset would be tonight.

It wasn't until I got back inside I realized that I had barely thought of how I was feeling all the way round and actually remembered feeling a bit of a fraud.

Covering the Bases

Could my attacks have been that bad all these years? Had I been imagining their severity? Later on I learnt about the apex effect, the fact that people often 'forget' the severity of their problem or even that they had one at all!

I got into the habit of walking around the block every day, come rain or shine, but was still nervous about venturing further, I didn't want to spoil things, push myself, in case it all went horribly wrong and I was again confined to the house having experienced the pleasure and sheer joy of being free but I soon realized I wasn't free until I pushed myself and tested to the limit.

I knew I had found a tool at last that worked, I had proved that, so set about ensuring that all my bases were covered and that when I walked into town alone I had covered every eventuality.

I tapped for:

- **Even though I am scared this is not going to work...**

- **Even though I'm scared I won't be able to get back home quick enough if it all goes horribly wrong...**
- **Even though I am frightened the whole thing is going to exhaust me and set me back years...**

I set myself a task of going into a supermarket and buying something, queuing up like a normal individual, paying for it and leaving without rushing out. I had learned many years ago that running away from the feeling of panic only compounded it in the long run and started to actually look forward to testing my new skill in the field, knowing I had something at last that would help.

I had experienced the under eye point as being especially helpful to me as it was always my stomach beginning to clench that heralded an attack and the under eye, being the stomach meridian, seemed to deal with this feeling nicely so I also knew I had an emergency tool should I get a bit overwhelmed at any point which helped enormously to get me out of the door!

So I walked into town, it wasn't all plain sailing but I felt myself welcoming the different feelings as a chance to practice and a sign that I was open to experiencing and dealing with these things and not just be rid of them, forevermore scared of them cropping up out of the blue again with the same forceful shock and effect on me they had had in the past.

I knew if I could do this feeling slightly wobbly but confident this was far more valuable than feeling nothing at all, and I was right, as I looked for more and wider experiences to test myself, literally shouting out for the feelings to come on in and do their worst, they stopped.

I had thought about looking for the initial cause of the panic attacks but somehow that didn't seem relevant or useful anymore but what I did do was tap for the weird empty feeling of them not being there any longer.

- **Even though it feels strange not having them around anymore...**
- **Even though I can't believe they've gone...**

I also tapped for the enormous loss of life I felt for the years I had missed doing 'normal' things especially with my daughter who I feel missed out dreadfully when she was young on so many different experiences.

- **Even though I am so sad I missed out...**
- **Even though I feel so guilty at making my little girl miss so many things...**
- **Even though I blame myself for her being so nervous now...**
- **Even though I know there is no way I can ever make up for this loss...**

I covered as much as I could of the guilt and the feelings of having been a dreadful coward all these years not to have tried harder and just done things anyway, however I felt, but I realize now that that just is not so, people who suffer panic attacks, if anything, are extremely strong and brave, going to war every day.

Some of the most courageous people I know are the ones who have suffered panic and anxiety attacks for most of their lives and have soldiered on regardless and this includes those who were not even able to leave their houses.

They still got up every morning to face the day with the fear of not knowing quite what to expect which is like being told to march into battle with no weapon, no map and just a vague knowing that there is a huge hostile army lurking somewhere.

You can do it and EFT will help you!

Basic EFT Anxiety Protocol - Step by Step

However, remember, EFT is not just a weapon to help you win this war, it is a finely crafted tool that will help you design and fashion the life you want in intricate and beautiful detail.

So, to sum up:

1. Walk through a situation in your mind first, tap on everything that comes up and use this to prepare for the actual event.
2. Try and notice as you are doing each round if there is a particular point that always seems to help or makes you feel better, this is a useful single point to tap if you are out and forget everything else!
3. Make small trips first to build confidence in yourself and the technique.
4. Make the statements very specific, concentrating first on your bodily sensations then including all your fears about having an attack.

5. Then really embrace the feelings and welcome them as a chance to practice; this was the key for me.

6. Lastly tidy up all the feelings about how things are now you are free of them and also if need be the loss of life involved.

Try it, if I can do it anyone can!

The Complete Emotional Freedom Techniques Protocol

The protocol itself looks complicated at first but is really very simple and is just the meridian points.

What you do is tap lightly on each of them, you get used to doing this very quickly, and when you have been using EFT for a while you can just do a few taps here and there, maybe on your collarbone or under your eye, for rapid relief.

Have a look at the diagram and just touch each point and as you work your way through them you will see there's a natural progression as you go down the body which makes them very easy to remember.

The EFT Treatment Points

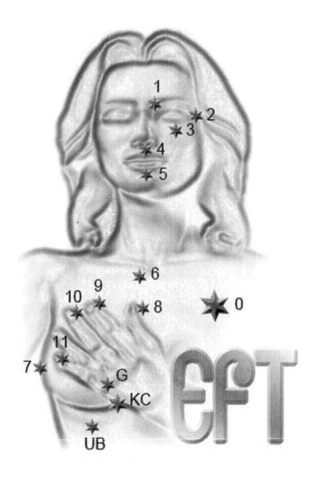

0   **The Sore Spot** - The area on your chest where you pin a brooch or medal. Gently feel around with your fingers and locate a spot that feels tender or slightly sore.

1   **The Start of the Eyebrow** (EB) - Where the bone of your eyebrow meets the bridge of your nose.

2   **The Side of the Eye** (SE) - On the bone at the corner of your eye.

3   **Under the Eye** (UE) - On the bone just under your eye, in line with your pupil when you are looking forward.

4   **Under the Nose** (UN) - Between your nose and your upper lip.

5   **Under the Mouth** (CH) - On your chin just below your lower lip.

6   **Collarbone** (CB) - In the angle formed by your collarbone and breastbone.

7   **Under Arm** (UA) - In line with a man's nipple or the middle of a woman's bra strap.

8   **Thumb** (Th) - All finger points are on the side of the finger and in line with the nail bed.

9   **Index Finger** (IF)

10   **Middle Finger** (MF)

11   **Little Finger** (LF)

K   **Karate Chop Point** (KP) - On the side of your hand.

G   **Gamut Point** (GP) - Just behind the knuckles of your ring and little finger.

UB **Under Breast** (UB) - Please note this is not a classic EFT point, and is not included in a normal round, but I have found it very useful in cases where anger is involved, either my own anger or when reacting to someone else's, so have included it here for your information.

Getting Started

In EFT these points are stimulated by gently tapping with your middle finger or middle and index finger combined. Tap quite rapidly; a good guide is about 7 to 9 taps while breathing in and out normally. Do not tap too hard, if you were tapping on a table the sound would be barely audible but you do need to feel the tap so do what feels right for you. However you do not want to end up bruised!

While familiarizing yourself with the points you may find that some feel tender and thus are easy to find. For example a lot of women find the point under the arm especially tender and higher than they think.

While you are tapping on different statements you may feel some points are particularly sore to the touch or that you feel different instantly while you are paying attention to a certain point.

Some people find a specific point always helps and this can be a valuable point to remember and use on its own when you are stressed and can't remember what to do. This is your emergency stop point.

And if any of the points feel too tender to tap simply hold them and massage gently instead, taking a deep breath in and out as you do so.

For practice now tap all the points starting from the Eyebrow point right down to the Karate Chop point, breathing gently all the time setting up a rhythm as you follow the sequence down your body. The order you tap in is not set in stone but is a nice way of remembering all the points.

Contacting the Problem

In EFT we use tapping the meridian points to release the interference and distortions that negative emotions cause and we do this by creating a statement spoken out loud to focus the mind as we tap each point.

So to begin with it is important to state the problem clearly and as you feel it, in your own words and how it applies to you personally.

Think of a problem, a fear, a pain, something that makes you feel sad or indeed any negative emotion that you would like to clear. The more honest you can be about how it makes you feel, the more profound the change will be.

- **I hate the way my heart flutters all the time.**
- **Not being able to go out on my own really upsets me.**
- **I can hardly breath.**

- I feel so exhausted.
- I can't think straight.
- Having to rely on other people drives me mad.
- This squirming feeling in my stomach.
- I feel like I'm going to die.
- I will never be able to cope with this.
- This is never going to end.
- I just can't do anything when I feel so bad.
- Everything is so dark and hopeless.
- I don't know how I'm going to get through the day.

The Set Up

Now that you have stated your problem you can start the Set Up

You create an Opening Statement by enclosing your problem in the following statement:

- **Even though (insert problem statement) I deeply and profoundly love and accept myself.**

So if your problem is 'I feel so bad about letting my family down' this would translate into:

- **Even though I feel bad about letting my family down I deeply and profoundly love and accept myself.**

Taking a SUDs Reading

Before commencing a round of tapping it is useful to ascertain what level of discomfort you are feeling so that you can instantly see what effect one round has had and whether you need to do more work on it, create a new statement, or if it has been completely cleared in one round. We call this taking a SUDS reading, which stands for Subjective Units of Disturbance or Distress.

Now you have the problem in mind, taking 0 as completely pain free, calm and happy and 10 being the highest amount of pain and distress imaginable, think of a number that would rate your feelings now. Just let the first number that comes into your head be your guide, do not struggle or argue with it.

Testing is a very important part of EFT and is what allows us to see just how quickly changes can be made which gives us enormous confidence in the process as well as ourselves.

Now you have your Set Up Statement, and also a guide as to the level of discomfort you are experiencing, it is time to start a round of EFT.

The Round

Now find the Sore Spot and while rubbing it gently say your Opening Statement three times while really concentrating on what you are saying and even if you do not feel totally comfortable with 'I deeply and profoundly love and accept myself' do try and sound meaningful, I promise you in time this will change but if you find it too difficult initially you can create an Opening Statement and deal with that first using:

- **Even though I find it difficult to say I deeply and profoundly love and accept myself I deeply and profoundly love and accept myself.**

Now it is time to tap each of the points, starting with the Eyebrow (EB) point and working all the way down to the Karate Chop (K) point while repeating a shortened version of your Opening Statement which is called the Reminder Phrase.

For example a Reminder Phrase for the Opening Statement:

Even though the kids' screaming is driving me crazy I deeply and profoundly love and accept myself...

...would be **'kids' screaming is driving me crazy'** which you say as you tap each point.

The 9 Gamut

After the Karate Chop point gently tap the Gamut Point on the back of the hand while doing the following:

1. move your eyes from the floor to the ceiling without moving your head and back again.

2. move your eyes from left to right and back again

3. move your eyes in a big circle and back again

4. hum a bar of a tune, like Happy Birthday or a few notes of a scale

5. count - one two three four five

6. hum again

Take a deep breath in and out.

These may seem slightly strange things to do but they have an effect on the brain by making it switch from side to side quickly in order to wake up your neurology and let the tapping work on the problem.

Make sure you try and keep the Reminder Phrase in mind as much as possible to keep you focused, it may seem tricky at first but doesn't take long to get used to the routine.

Now repeat the Round one more time, tapping all the points from the Eyebrow to the Karate Chop point finishing with a deep breath and just give yourself time to think about how you are now feeling.

Now you have done what is often referred to as the Complete EFT Sandwich, two Rounds of tapping with the 9 Gamut in the middle.

Feedback

This is now the time to take another SUDs reading and see by how much your level of discomfort or distress has dropped.

Don't be disheartened if it started at, say, 8 and is not down to 0 completely but is now at a 4, this is progress indeed and you have already reduced your bad feelings by half!

Do another complete round using either of these statements.

- **Even though there is still some of the problem left...**
- **Even though I still have some of this problem...**

If there is just a tiny amount left, say you have reduced your SUDs to a 2 or lower, you can use:

- **I want to completely overcome this problem and I deeply and profoundly love and accept myself.**

And that really is all there is to it!

It is very difficult to get anything wrong. You may find it necessary to refine your Opening Statement or create a new one if you find the original problem has not been shifted but all tapping stimulates the meridians and has a calming effect on the entire system so don't be afraid to try different statements until you find the one that works for each problem you are working on.

Step One – Preparing To Go Out

Now you are familiar with the EFT Sequence it is time to walk through a situation in your mind, tapping on every feeling that comes up and using this to prepare for the actual event.

If you are not comfortable using the sequence yet please go back and practice.

I want you to think about going out now (or whatever event causes you to panic). Think about the very first preparations you need to make, finding your shoes, putting on your coat etc. Notice how you are feeling physically and where you are affected by this and tap this down to zero using an appropriate Opening Statement such as:

- **Even though I have butterflies in my tummy...**
- **Even though my heart is beating really fast...**

- **Even though I feel sick at the thought of going out…**

Not getting any response?

Ok, so how would you feel if I said, for this to work you have to go outside right now and stand on the pavement outside your house? Did you feel anything then?

Now work with that feeling, get it right down to zero, and if there is more than one symptom treat each one using a different Opening Statement.

Be sure to take a SUDS reading so you are aware how things are going, this is very important to encourage you to go on.

- ***Please note***: It is possible to reduce your SUDS by tapping just one round from the EB to the KC point without doing the 9 Gamut procedure. I only used to use the 9 Gamut when a number refused to budge; people vary, try it with and without and see what works best for you.

50

Now imagine every single stage of getting ready to go out;

- **Finding your shoes and putting them on.**
- **Reaching up for your coat.**
- **Finding your keys.**
- **Walking to the front door and opening it.**

Now when you feel ready, and have tapped any bad feelings down to zero, in your mind's eye step out of your front door, walk down the path, stand outside your house for a moment and then walk once around your block.

Notice every little detail of how this makes you feel and tap on each of the feelings

- **Even though reaching for the front door makes me shake...**
- **Even though walking down the path makes my knees turn to jelly...**

- **Even though I have these knots in my stomach...**

I cannot emphasize often enough how important this step is.

It is also an excellent way to prepare for any stressful situation or one that causes panic, such as going to an interview, driving test, asking your boss for a raise.

Emergency Stop Point

And it's a good means of seeing if there is one particular tapping point where you notice a shift on more than one occasion and which you can then use as your emergency stop point.

My emergency stop point is the under eye (UE) point which coincidentally (or not!) is directly connected to the stomach meridian, where I used to feel the panic first rising from.

Any one of the points is a likely candidate but don't get disheartened if you do not find one straight away, for some it takes a while. A complete round of EFT only takes moments so don't despair if you don't ever find one, you don't need the added stress of thinking you have failed at identifying your emergency stop point!

Calming Points

If you haven't managed to find your emergency stop point there are three points you can tap which many have found calms them instantly so are handy to know and I have included them in the Be Calm Now Checklist at the back.

UE – Under eye
UA – Under arm
CB - Collarbone

Step Two – Going Out

Now you have mind-walked a trip around your block and cleared all the feelings it is time to actually go out. If you are starting to feel bad about going out you really haven't completed the first step as that is designed to relieve any apprehension about the actual trip, so please go back and do it now.

You will now be well practiced at tapping a round of EFT and as you prepare to go out and actually walk around your block will be able to tap from the EB to the KC point if you feel any familiar sensations beginning to appear. While you are out it is not necessary to think about Opening Statements; if you need to, just tap on the feelings:

- **My fluttering heart.**
- **My tight throat.**
- **My wobbly knees.**

Touch and Breath

You may also find it helps to simply hold or massage each point gently while taking a deep breath in and out, this prevents any unnecessary shuddering while in a heightened state of alert which is not helpful; many also tap far too hard when they feel panic rising thinking the harder they tap the quicker the anxiety will subside, this is not the case, stimulation of the point is all that is necessary; and you don't want to bruise yourself. This is also an excellent way to use EFT covertly while outside without drawing attention to yourself!

Ok, so you have been out, yes? I wish I was there now to pat you on the back and tell you how well you have done and how this is just the beginning, there is so much more you can do.

No, you didn't make it out? Why? What happened? Did you get to the front door, make it down the path, walk a little way?

Tap now for how you are feeling about it all.

- **Even though I feel overwhelmed…**
- **Even though this can't possibly work for me…**
- **Even though I feel I have failed…**

Then try again.

And even when you have walked around your block feeling relaxed, keep doing it, every day, even when you go further afield it's good to do this for a while, the simple things are good daily reminders of progress and how far you have come!

Step Three - Challenging Yourself

One of the most important things for me was not sitting back for too long at any stage and letting myself feel too self-satisfied. I built on each achievement steadily and pushed myself as often as I could. The more I did it the less tiring it was and became so much easier, just an initial push each time, then delight at the results.

And the brilliant thing is that each time I did something it was not nearly as bad as I had remembered or could imagine because I was **different** now so couldn't possibly know how I would feel.

Keep challenging yourself to new situations. They don't need to be huge leaps, stretch your comfort zone a little at a time, you can tell if you are doing so by the need to tap to quieten your system.

In fact I want you to put yourself in a position where you **need** to tap every day. I want you to welcome situations where this is necessary, a chance to practice and stretch yourself giving you confidence to go further knowing you have the perfect tool, literally at your fingertips, to do this.

At one point I stopped drinking coffee, which seemed sensible, as the caffeine was triggering panic attacks at that time, but I later used this rather dramatic effect when I was thinking of ways to challenge myself and find ways to practice.

I would actually drink a cup of espresso and practice dealing with the feelings it caused, the absolute classic feeling of rising panic with racing heart. Fantastic progress was made in the privacy and safety of my own home and I used walking, then running, up and down stairs in the same way with equal success.

So now you have walked around the block plan to go further, into town, firstly with someone if this was impossible before or the least bit stressful, and when you can do this comfortably then go on your own. Little steps, further each day is what did it for me. There is no need to make a grand gesture and exhaust yourself (although some choose to do it that way!)

Do you still feel afraid? Try tapping on:

- **Even though I used to be afraid I want a brand new future…**

Now how does that feel?

But, one big mistake I made was thinking I had to do everything I was asked to do, that it was my duty. I soon wore myself out doing things I really didn't want to because I felt I should do them for practice and that if I didn't I would be using the panics as an excuse to get out of them.

Please do not fall into this trap. If necessary tap to see if you should undertake this request to go out and do something. There are some challenges that are just not worth doing and certainly if they are things you do not like or will not continue pursuing, then just don't.

For instance, once when I had arranged to go somewhere but there were engineering works on the railway line that weekend (meaning a half hour train journey then transfer to a bus for a 40 minute ride to my destination) I thought, now come on, last week you did a 2 hour train ride to London, you can do that or are you just using this as an excuse not to go?

Then I thought, no, I hate buses, I do not intend to use them in the future so there is no good reason why I should do this at all and stayed at home instead, no guilt, nothing, a bit of relief but that's ok, **people who don't panic feel relieved at not doing stuff too!**

If you don't like roller coasters don't go on one, but if you want to experience one, and see what all the fuss is about, you **can** now!

Loss of Life

The buzz of the new freedom I was experiencing which seemed to have come about so easily, was, after a while, tempered with feelings of dreadful sadness as I realised what I had missed out on and how I had badly affected my loved ones with my behaviour.

For a while it seemed getting better too quickly was disrespectful of everybody's experiences and I felt this guilt and sadness may be holding back my progress so I dealt with it using several Opening Statements such as:

- **Even though I feel so bad about everybody missing out because of my fear...**
- **Even though I feel so guilty at not having tried harder...**
- **Even though I feel so sad my little girl missed so much when she was growing up...**
- **Even though I wish things had been so different...**

The effect that feelings of loss of life can have on you should not be underestimated; what you have missed out on, places you have not been, the dreams you dared not have can be devastating and the sadness and grief can cut you to your very core.

This is an extremely important part of recovery, and needs dealing with now. You may use a general phrase such as:

- **Even though I grieve for all the experiences I've missed...**
- **Even though I am so sad I will never know what I have missed...**

Or you may be very specific:

- **Even though I am so sad I missed my mother's funeral...**
- **Even though I am so angry with myself I turned down that job...**

It's Only An Adrenaline Allergy!

Adrenaline is a wonderful thing, not only from the fight or flight aspect, which is a built in survival tool, but adrenaline also leads us to a state of clarity of thought and awareness which is second to none and actually gives us **more** control over our bodies than at any other time.

Think of a female lion stalking her prey, moving close to the ground, very particular, controlled movements, making tiny adjustments in response to her environment, alert and ready but also willing to wait for the optimum time for a successful kill.

Her body is pumped full of adrenaline, but is her heart palpitating? No. Is her gut churning with fear? No. Is she shaking? No. Is she making funny noises and flapping her paws helplessly, desperate to get away from the situation? No.

She is focused, aware and in perfect control.

So why do we get the symptoms of palpitations, shaking, dry mouth, shivers when adrenaline is released into our systems?

BECAUSE WE HAVE AN ADRENALINE ALLERGY!

This is the only possible explanation and the good news is all allergies are treatable and the even better news is that EFT is especially good for this.

So watch out for adrenaline spikes and treat them immediately with a round of tapping from the EB to the KC points on

- **It's only an adrenaline allergy.**

You may notice, as a lot of us did when we first started looking at this, that your general background level of adrenaline from day to day is elevated and in this state of hypervigilance your response to the smallest of spikes is what takes you over the rooftops but this will soon settle down as you treat the allergy more and more.

Also, I want you to remember that thoughts follow on from feelings, and not the other way around, when you are in a state of heightened hypervigilance so you must not pay any attention to what you are thinking, it is not true. You are not going to die, always be like this, look silly. And please do not make any important decisions either about yourself or your life while in that state.

Daily Symptoms and How To Deal With Them

People who suffer from panic and anxiety attacks also experience an array of annoying symptoms every day. These range from feeling depressed to having frequent headaches, bad sleeping patterns, loss of appetite, bad digestion; the list is endless.

Many find that as the anxiety clears these also disappear but I have found it extremely beneficial to treat them as soon as they crop up. This not only helps to get rid of these irritations quicker but also helps with general relaxation levels which is always a good thing.

As soon as I felt a headache coming on a couple of taps under the eye relieved it almost instantly.

- **Even though my head is starting to thump...**

If I lay thrashing about in bed unable to sleep, thoughts spiralling out of control I would tap a round. If nothing else it gave me something to do and broke the destructive loop.

- **Even though I can't sleep...**
- **Even though thrashing around is exhausting me...**
- **Even though I don't know why I can't sleep, I am so tired...**

If I woke feeling depressed that I wasn't making quicker progress I would tap on that too.

- **Even though I feel I am never going to get through this...**
- **Even though I don't feel I'm up to this...**
- **Even though my whole life is shit and even getting rid of the panics won't make it any better...**

When I didn't feel like eating or my stomach was upset I would deal with it there and then.

- **Even though I can't be bothered to eat this meal...**
- **Even though the thought of eating this food is making me feel sick...**
- **Even though I have this burning in my tummy...**

In fact I got into the habit of doing a quick round as I was sitting down to eat and whatever your particular pet problem may be try doing a round routinely **before** it gets too bad.

Clearing the Worst Panic
Attacks From the Past

I t's important to go back and visit your worst panic attacks, maybe it was the very first one, and deal with it, clear the emotional charge from it.

Mine was on a train and even though I wasn't having attacks anymore every time I went on a train I felt uneasy, as if they may come back, and every time I had successfully completed a journey I breathed a huge sigh of relief.

Use this phrasing:

- **Even though I panicked on a train this is now in the past…**
- **Even though I freaked out at the bottom of the Empire State building this is now in the past…**

Pinpoint your worst panics and deal with them, NOW.

Getting to Know Yourself

A really good way to get to know yourself and your responses is to tap gently and thoughtfully on each point while concentrating on one particular thing and see how each feels.

Say for example you have a headache, start tapping on the eyebrow (EB), continue tapping on that point slowly. While you focus on your feelings and see if that point has something to do with your headache. Continue with each point and see if you make any connections.

I found the under eye point was very specific for my stomach churning and still turn to that first, a few auspicious taps there has been a godsend to me in so many circumstances.

This technique can be used with anything, persistent unwanted thoughts and feelings as well as physical discomforts and is an excellent way of finding your emergency point to use when you get a bit flustered and can't think what to do.

Self Esteem

It's understandable to think because you are anxious and panic that you are a coward, stupid even, but this is just not so. As we have seen, elevated levels of adrenaline make us think things that are completely untrue and this extends to how we feel about ourselves.

Some of the bravest people I know have suffered panic attacks everyday and have carried on their lives regardless.

You are not a worm or a weasel and you need to get rid of this idea right now.

- **Even though I think I am pathetic...**
- **Even though I am the most useless person I know...**
- **Even though I am a worm...**
- **Even though I despise myself for being so weak...**
- **Even though I am a coward...**

- **Even though I hate myself for not trying harder...**

And as far as the last opening statement is concerned, remember this -

YOU COULD ONLY DO WHAT YOU
COULD DO.

IF YOU COULD HAVE DONE IT ANY
OTHER WAY YOU WOULD HAVE DONE.

And now you **can** do it differently, you have a way, you have help, you have a tool that gives you the confidence to go back into life and really live it without being scared anymore.

Avoiding Decisions

People who have panic attacks invariably have a problem making decisions, it seems to be a structural thing but one that can be dealt with using EFT very effectively.

I had so many ifs and buts running round my system every time I tried to do something, I just couldn't make a decent decision about anything when I was at my worst, even down to whether or not to use toothpaste one night as I couldn't be sure that wasn't making me feel worse just before bed.

Try one of these:

- **Even though I don't know what to do...**
- **Even though I can't be sure I am making the right choice...**
- **Even though I am crap at making decisions...**

- **Even though I am scared what to choose...**

Or make one up of your own but really get the SUDS down to zero, it helps in so many ways and is well worth doing, believe me.

You can even tap when faced with a decision to help you decide on the spot such as:

- **Even though I can't decide between the blue or black jacket...**
- **Even though I don't know if I want a sandwich or soup for lunch...**
- **Even though I really can't decide whether to wash up or hoover first...**

Fear of Confrontation

As with the fear of decisions those who suffer from anxiety have a great fear of confrontation and this needs to be addressed.

It doesn't matter if it's facing your kids, your husband or your boss, any situation where you have to assert yourself is considered confrontational. And as with most anxious people you will wait until crisis point and then find yourself ranting incoherently, which achieves nothing and goes to reaffirm that you are rubbish at confrontation.

But, if you can take the anxiety out, you will be able to 'confront' the other party well before your threshold is breached and you can do it calmly and rationally and will be surprised at the responses you then receive.

Kids do actually react quite well to calm requests as do spouses and even bosses!

- Even though speaking up for myself makes me shake...
- Even though the thought of asking Jim not to make me look small in front of other people makes me feel sick...
- Even though my boss scares me...
- Even though asking my boss for a raise makes me feel weak in the knees...
- Even though I can't complain about bad service in shops...
- Even though the kids don't even listen to me...
- Even though no one listens to me...
- Even though no one takes any notice of me...

Special Circumstances

Panic in Bed

I used to get particularly stressed out when I felt a panic attack coming on in bed. At first I thought all hope was lost, if I could no longer feel safe and relaxed while I was in my one sanctuary, there was nowhere left to go, the end was surely near, but now I know differently and really wish I had had someone to explain this to me then, it would have saved me years of going into myself further as I began to think I was losing my mind.

The thing is that when you are at rest, with none of the daily distractions, your thoughts and fears become uppermost in your mind and if you are in an already hypervigilant state your body will respond with the usual panic symptoms, it is as simple as that.

It is a natural response, even waking from a dream feeling you are panicking is just your body responding quite normally, there is no need to freak out at this as I used to, even people who don't have panic attacks can wake in the middle of the night with a pounding heart after a dream they can't remember.

Just concentrate on your bodily symptoms and feelings.

- **Even though my heart is pounding...**
- **Even though I can hardly breath...**
- **Even though I am shaking...**
- **Even though my throat feels so tight...**

This will calm your system down sufficiently enough to return to sleep. You may want to tap for:

- **Even though I am scared of having a panic in bed...**
- **Even though I am scared I will wake panicking...**

Panic in the Bath

And the same applies to the bath as in bed, it is a time of tranquillity, time out for yourself and in this calm space uncomfortable thoughts can bubble up and cause panic symptoms, as can the heat of the bath itself as the body naturally responds to the changes in body temperature.

At one point I would panic as I started to take my clothes off for a bath, you may not be this bad but a few rounds of EFT will calm the energy system so you can get the full benefit of the relaxing bath itself!

And remember, when you are in a hypervigilant state, none of your thoughts have any truth to them and this is a very good thing to first tap on.

- **Even though I think junk when I am scared...**
- **Even though the thought of getting into a bath frightens me...**
- **Even though I panic in the bath...**

- **Even though I think I may fall and drown...**
- **Even though I am scared no one will hear me if I need help to get out...**

Panic on a Plane

Now, it is well known that people who don't normally suffer from panic attacks can react very badly to plane travel but for someone with panics you would think it would be even worse, and it can be, but with EFT you can really show everyone else how it is done!

If you have to do a plane trip treat it like any other situation by planning ahead. Really imagine every stage of the trip in your mind, from check-in, to waiting in the departure lounge, to queuing to get on the plane, sitting in your seat waiting for take off, using the small toilet on the plane, pushing past people, landing, getting your luggage; do the whole thing in your mind until each part of the trip is down to zero.

Tap for turbulence on the plane, delays at the airport, cover as much as you can, then deal with the thought that none of this is going to work.

- **Even though I hate queuing...**
- **Even though I hate waiting around...**
- **Even though I hate not being in control of the situation...**
- **Even though none of this is going to work...**
- **Even though I can never see myself getting on a plane...**

Panic in a Lift

And again, many people who never have problems with anxiety cannot use lifts and this is another good way to test your new skill.

Imagine standing in front of a lift now and tap your feelings about getting into it down to zero. Really feel the doors closing behind you, that small space, the heady, slightly rushing feeling as it ascends rapidly, the fear of it breaking down and you getting trapped in there and having to be rescued.

- **Even though lifts scare the hell out of me...**
- **Even though I am frightened I will get trapped in there...**
- **Even though I hate being so close to people in such a small space...**
- **Even though I am scared I will get trapped and need the loo...**
- **Even though I hate the feeling of everything closing in on me...**

Please bear in mind that knowing and using EFT does not mean you will never feel anxious ever again, it means you will no longer be scared of anxiety because you have the resources to deal with it swiftly and efficiently.

Everyone gets nervous about some things, everyone's pulse rises at certain times, everyone feels sick at the thought of some things but with EFT you can get back to the normal highs and lows of everyday living confident that you will never again be overwhelmed by them.

Treating the Fear of Future Panics

What are the things that still frighten you? Is it the thought of having a panic attack out of the blue? Is there a particular situation in which you are scared it will happen?

I want you now to dig around and see what you can find and treat it.

- **Even though I am terrified a panic attack is going to creep up on me...**
- **Even though I am scared when I get stressed out it will happen again...**
- **Even though I am scared I will forget what to do...**
- **Even though I am scared when I visit my mother it will all come back...**

We are not trying to push towards a state where we don't need to tap any more. Everyday there are moments that make our hearts flutter, little excitements, the highs that make our hearts sing, we do not want to eliminate these, in fact on the contrary we want to be able to allow these back into our lives without thinking they herald a panic attack.

I got to the stage where even watching a quiz show was too much for me, the apprehension as to whether the contestants would get the questions right was unbearable and would make me very anxious and at that time I started closing down to the smallest possible stimulus just in case it triggered an attack.

For years I sought ways to stop rising feelings of panic when I was getting excited. When I had visitors I could feel the overwhelm coming on of trying to tell an interesting story and getting carried away by the rising excitement. Sometimes I would have to stop and just sit and listen to them talking, control my breathing, and hope I could continue in a while. It was very frustrating.

I tapped on trying to stop being scared of feelings that would trigger an attack, but it just wasn't specific enough, then I hit upon anticipation as being the beginning of overwhelm and that worked a treat.

So my one and all time most profoundly life changing opening statement must be –

- **Even though I am scared that my feelings of anticipation and excitement will overwhelm me and turn into panic I deeply and profoundly love and accept myself.**

When the fear of panic attacks has gone you can then risk feeling a shiver of delight at the smallest of things, or feeling your whole system being elevated at the beauty of a sunset, or the touch of a lover.

This is what we want to get back to, being able to feel, to respond to the world around us without being scared of ourselves and our reactions.

So remember, I'm not saying you will never need to tap again. I use EFT daily for minor irritations, calming myself down BEFORE they spiral into something big. It can be as simple as tapping away the annoyance of being interrupted for the umpteenth time by a telesales person during a TV programme, or a neighbour's dog incessantly barking or when the washing machine floods.

You have the tool now, don't be scared to use it for even the smallest thing, every time you tap your energy system is soothed.

And remember –

IT'S OK TO FEEL STRANGE IN A STRANGE SITUATION!

More Tips and Useful Techniques

EmoTrance

I was on a train once, it was a particularly long and tedious journey, I was tired and the carriage filled up with noisy school children. I wasn't exactly panicking but started to feel very uncomfortable and stressed out.

Their screams and shouts were jarring me and I could feel my breathing getting heavier but instead of tapping I decided to experiment and consciously channelled all the energy of those school children in through the top of my head and down through my body, just to see what it would feel like.

And my god what a difference it made, I felt instant compassion for those children, I felt I could understand exactly where they were coming from, so to speak, and all irritation just vanished.

I mention this because a couple of weeks ago I was in the Post Office, it was very busy, I was overdressed and getting very hot and flustered, people milling around all over the place and I remembered the train experience and once again channelled the energy of the people around me straight into the top of my head and again felt an instant sense of alignment and peace with my surroundings rather than irritation and apprehension.

This is a very important part of recovery and reorientation as you ease yourself back into the world, allowing experiences in rather than continually shielding yourself from them.

Exactly What Is EmoTrance?

Channelling energy in through the top of the head is not classic EmoTrance, for that you would have a bad feeling and say:

- **Where do I feel that in my body?**

…and deal with the sensation, wherever it is, by softening and flowing the energy out of the body, but, once you get the hang of EmoTrance (which is incredibly easy) you will find you can do all sorts of things with energy.

So, next is a simple exercise to introduce you to the power and wonder of EmoTrance.

Simple EmoTrance Demonstration

Try this now.

Think of something that would make you feel bad. If you can't think of something yourself straight away use.

You are a useless waste of space!

Now write it down on a piece of paper.

Now notice where you feel that in your body, place your hands there, and now soften that feeling and with your intention, as intention alone moves energy, decide to move that energy out of your body and now watch where that energy starts to flow, notice where that channel is.

There is a natural exit point for that energy, that feeling, to leave your body, so just notice where that is as the energy smoothly, easily and cleanly flows out of your body.

When you feel the energy has completely gone look at the statement on the paper again and let that feeling flow in and out once again. Now make it quicker, energy in and out, in and out, until it is really zipping through you.

When you end up feeling a lightness, to some a tingling, and when you are laughing as it flows quickly through you, then you have reached the energized end state. A marvellous feeling that once experienced, with even your worst fears, makes you invincible!

Now give yourself a big pat on the back, well done!

So, from the top...

You have a bad feeling.

Show me with your hands

Where does it want to go?

Soften and flow
It's only an energy!

If you have any problems getting started I really do recommend consulting an EmoTrance practitioner[*]. Just one session can get you going and once you have experienced ET in action and achieved the energized end state, where the energy is literally zipping through you and energizing your whole system, you will find it happening quite automatically on occasions.

---

[*] Visit http://emotrance.com for full listing of all certified practitioners

When To Use EmoTrance

Any time you get a bad feeling! BUT the brilliant thing with EmoTrance is that it goes much much further than that. Once you have mastered the basic technique you can use it for all manner of things. Just think 'energy nutrition', sucking in all the energies around you and experiencing the energy of a sunset just as greedily as eating a tasty nourishing meal!

The Power of Self Forgiveness

We have dealt with loss of life and the sadness for all you have missed out on and for the difficulties you may have caused your family and friends but one important thing to do is to forgive yourself for feeling the way you do. And I mean here not just for beating yourself up constantly for not being braver but for every single instance of fear and panic that you experience.

I remember once getting het up and anxious when a piano tuner was about to arrive. I really wasn't sure what to tap on, there was no obvious cause or anything particular I could put my finger on to create an opening statement from. I started pacing, felt my chest tightening and my pulse racing and began to walk quietly and meditatively in an attempt to calm down while taking some deep breaths. I felt under pressure as he would be arriving any minute which worsened things.

Then I heard myself saying, Why do I keep doing this to myself, what is wrong with me? And at that moment I stopped and simply forgave myself for being so stressed out. I felt a movement of energy, the bad feelings shifted down a channel somewhere through my middle. And then they were gone.

Simply forgiving myself had had an incredibly powerful effect, instantly.

So try that now, forgive yourself for all the times you have made yourself feel bad. Notice where that feeling goes, it will be the same sensation every time you do it. And from now on make a promise to forgive yourself every time you start feeling anxious or get stressed out and see just how quickly those bad feelings are dispelled.

You may also want to do a round of EFT saying I forgive myself for…

Three EmoTrance Exercises

Learning To Follow With Intention

1. Touch or have another touch you lightly with one fingertip on the arm or some other part of your body.
2. Have them lightly massage or tap the area.
3. Follow the touch as it travels through your system with your intention.
4. Repeat on different parts of your body until such touches flow instantly and smoothly.

Emotional Healing Exercise

1. Call up an old emotion you know well and which you can feel in your body.
2. Where do you feel this in your body? Show me with your hands.
3. Place your hands and your attention there and consider where this energy would want to go. Assist it in softening and

beginning to flow through its rightful channels, whatever they may be, all the way through and out.

4. Re-call the original experience and repeat until it flows instantly and cleanly, and the original 'emotional pain' is no more.

5. You know the problem is truly healed when instead of pain you experience a pleasurable, charging sensation (the 'energised end state' - beyond mere symptom cessation).

Feasting On Energy

1. Find any object, person, plant, animal, landscape, music, work of art, weather, etc. and tune into its energy.

2. Drop any shields you might have to this 'incoming energy'.

3. Where do you feel it in your body? Where does it need to go?

4. Assist in flowing it freely through its requisite channels, all the way through and out.

Breathing

Breathing may sound obvious but it was the first thing I stopped doing as soon as I felt anxious; I held my breath, in the classic shock way, so it is a good idea to really consciously make yourself breath slowly and deeply whenever you get a bit het up and this goes nicely with doing a brief tap on

- **It's only an adrenaline allergy.**

People who suffer from anxiety and panic attacks almost always breath shallowly, even when you tell them to take a deep breath you always find they do it from their chest. This not only gives the feeling of not getting enough air so you breath even quicker but also results in the characteristic tightness of the chest and heart area which can be so frightening. Chest pain and anxiety is very scary, and presuming you have checked with your doctor to rule out a physical cause, can easily be stopped using deep abdominal breathing.

Put your hand on your chest now and take a deep breath, do you feel your hand moving?

Now put your hand on your abdomen, take another deep breath, slowly, and make a real effort to push that hand out as far as possible as you are doing so, now exhale and feel your hand moving back. That is abdominal breathing, how you should be breathing all the time and now I will tell you why.

Why Bad Breathing Causes Anxiety and Panic Attacks

Rapid shallow breathing causes hyperventilation and this happens when more carbon dioxide is breathed out than the body is able to manufacture. Symptoms include dizziness, tingling, tightness of the chest with rapid heartbeat, feelings of unreality and an inability to think clearly. Does that sound familiar?

Then in a rapid downward spiral these hideous feelings then make you breathe even quicker causing the symptoms to worsen even further.

And there we have it, a classic anxiety and panic spiral which is very difficult to get out of and afterwards the exhaustion and feelings of being a limp rag combine with utter devastation and defeat and lead to ever increasing despair and phobias.

Breathing into a brown paper bag is a way of helping once the spiral has been embarked upon but a better way is to get into the habit of breathing correctly ALL the time so you never get to the point where you need to do that.

You may ask how can just breathing correctly help my anxiety and panic attacks?

Think about it, what you fear most are those awful feelings, the palpitations that come on for no reason, the dizziness, wobbliness, weak knees, feelings of unreality and not knowing what to do because you cannot even think straight, well if you knew how to prevent those from happening there would be nothing to fear, right?

Symptoms of Shallow Breathing and Hyperventilation

When you breathe shallowly and rapidly you lose too much carbon dioxide and your blood becomes too alkaline which causes havoc within your system as you can see from the list below and your body also gets a huge hit of adrenaline to try and right this which adds a further burden. Recognize any of these?

* Dizziness
* Lightheadedness
* Vertigo
* Feeling faint
* Blurred vision
* Headaches
* Palpitations
* Missed heartbeats
* Chest pain and feelings of constriction
* Difficulty breathing
* Lump in the throat
* Tightness of the throat

* Dry mouth
* Twitching limbs
* Tingling in fingers and toes
* Numbness of extremities
* Prickly feeling over the face and arms
* Nausea and vomiting
* Stomach pain with gas
* Weakness and exhaustion
* Severe apprehension and nervousness
* Fear of dying and/or going mad
* Paranoia
* Feelings of unreality
* Feeling out of control.

They're exactly the same symptoms of anxiety and panic attacks! Now do you see what I mean?

BREATHING PROPERLY FROM THE ABDOMEN PREVENTS ALL OF THOSE!

It's been proposed that panic attacks are purely a hyperventilation phenomenon, now I don't know about that, it may or may not be true, but it does make sense to me that if you know shallow and rapid breathing, when you get anxious, causes those things then having a way to prevent them happening will stop the cycle of fear of having the attacks.

So whatever triggers the feelings of anxiety or panic, it does not matter, the terrible physical feelings just will not happen!

How To Breathe Abdominally

You may have got exactly what I am talking about from the brief description above but if not and you are having problems try lying down and placing a book on your abdomen, the area between your ribs and your navel, and really try and push the book up as you breathe in.

Another way to see if what you are doing is right it to put your hands lightly on your lower ribs and watch your fingertips move apart at each in breath and move back as you breathe out.

Remember to always inhale through your nose though you may exhale through your nose or mouth, nose is better although if you do breath out through your mouth purse your lips slightly as if you are blowing out a candle, I found this helped me not to take the next breath through my mouth which is a bad habit I have and leads to overbreathing.

Of course it's good to keep your shoulders and chest area as relaxed as possible but even in the beginning I found it difficult not to relax and additionally breathing abdominally completely stopped that nasty feeling I get in my throat when I breath from my chest rapidly.

How to Slow Your Breathing Right Down

Now, you are aiming for 6 to 10 breaths a minute, anxious people chest breath at a rate of between 20 and 30 breaths a minute so part of the practice is to substantially slow your breathing down.

Look at the second hand of a watch and breath in for 3 seconds and out for 3. You really want to aim for 4 seconds or even more but don't push yourself to start with. You can also hold your breath for a few seconds before exhaling which has a really nice stabilizing effect and gives a real sense of control.

Have you noticed after a couple of deep abdominal breaths how steady you're feeling?

Retraining Your Breathing to Overcome Anxiety and Panic Attacks

The first thing you have to do is start watching your breathing throughout the day. Look out for times you notice your chest rising and falling as you breathe and also for the times your hold your breath while doing something. I noticed myself holding my breath the other day when I was painting and must have been thinking unconsciously that doing that would keep my hand steadier for drawing some lines.

Big mistake! I ended up dizzy and disorientated and couldn't work out why and of course my lines were wigglier than ever!

Whenever you catch yourself breathing from your chest make a real effort to take a couple of deep abdominal breaths. Also try and link this breathing to something you do regularly, like making a cup of tea and practice while the kettle boils.

To start with be gentle on yourself and just do a couple of breaths at a time, you don't want to frighten yourself or get anxious as it is possible that until you are used to breathing this way naturally you may feel a little dizzy to begin with but this is only from the fresh oxygen and not hyperventilation which is really quite difficult if not impossible to do when abdominal breathing so don't get too worried!

I have found even when the thought of something that makes me anxious kicks in, taking two or three abdominal breaths really does the trick and that's the key, doing it early enough in the cycle to prevent things getting any worse.

What you are aiming for is to learn deep relaxed slow abdominal breathing even when you are not thinking about it.

If you follow my advice by watching your breathing in the day and deliberately taking a couple of abdominal breaths when you notice you are chest breathing or holding your breath or starting to feel anxious very soon you will be doing it quite naturally.

And if you need any more convincing that breathing properly has a major influence on eradicating anxiety and panic here is a letter from an ordinary chap who happened upon my site while searching for help on the internet.

"Dear Nicola,

I have been having anxiety problems for the past few years over the smallest things that most people won't have problems about, like talking in a social setting, meeting new people, going out onto a social gathering. When I get anxious I would experience shortness of breath, lightheadedness, which would make me more anxious, thus creating a cycle of anxiety and breathlessness.

On one event the cycle of anxiety and breathlessness became so vicious I experienced hyperventilation and had my only panic attack ever, resulting in a trip to the hospital. This was two years ago. The anxiety problem went away for a while after I learnt to be bolder in social settings but it came back recently and it has put me on edge, this time it's different because I am more anxious about my breathing than being in a social setting. I would constantly feel short of breath during the day, sometimes gasping for air after a few flights of stairs, or feeling out of breath while talking to

119

others. The scary thing is I would feel light pains in my heart and chest area and that freaks me out because the fear of chest or heart problems is so consuming. I even thought I would die.

I was going to have my body checked when I came across your site and read your article on Breathing. I followed your technique on deep breathing and I instantly feel very energised and relaxed. I even tried walking up and down the stairs a few times and had no problems doing so anymore! Your techniques worked like a charm. I also realise now that all my panic attack problems, anxiety problems are all related in some way to breathing shallowly in the past. I have taken control back over my life by learning to breath deeply.

Thank You Nicola, your article is wonderful and it has saved my life!

Cheers,
Martin Kan"

Checklist to Stop Anxiety and Panic Attacks with Your Breathing

1. Practice abdominal breathing when you are feeling quite calm and relaxed so you know you are doing it correctly.
2. Slow your breaths down to 6 to 10 breaths a minute by using a watch.
3. Notice when you are shallow breathing or when you hold your breath and immediately take a couple of deep abdominal breaths.
4. When you start to feel anxious just remember to push your stomach out as you take a breath.

Above all don't get discouraged and practice when you are feeling good and you will start feeling bad less and less often and brilliant in no time at all!

Essential Oils

I remember standing on a beach once, a little sample bottle of an oil blend in my pocket, and as the waves roared towards me and I felt a little anxious I opened the bottle and inhaled deeply, thinking to myself, whatever you throw at me I can now cope with it. And to this day I take that little bottle out with me and sniff it now and then and that same feeling of strength and certainty always returns.

It doesn't matter what the oil is, mine was a particularly lovely blend called Peace and Calming a friend had sent me; choose a scent that feels right for you.

Since first writing this I have found out that smell directly affects the amygdala which is responsible for fear and panic and sends out signals to the adrenal glands to start pumping out adrenaline for initiating the fight or flight response.

As smell bypasses the cerebral cortex, and goes straight to the amygdala, in essence what we have here is a beautiful device to halt the fear response, **even when you are not thinking clearly**.

In fact you don't need to think at all, you just have to remember to smell something wonderful, preferably a scent that is associated with good memories, though just one you find lovely will do.

You can either take the bottle out with you to sniff, if it's an oil, or you can place a few drops on a cottonwool pad, wrapped in a tissue, and put it in a little ziplock bag to put in your pocket or handbag. Perfect.

While on the subject of essential oils I'd like to tell you about a client who had started having panic attacks following an extended period of using speed (amphetamines).

After working with him for a while he still had a very severe startle response which I believe was caused by the vast amounts of speed he had been using for many years.

At the time I was assisting Silvia Hartmann with the research for her new approach to aromatherapy and she suggested that a specific oil may help to heal the original damage caused by the overuse of amphetamines, that an oil may be able to heal the deep pathways that the speed had created in that person's brain.

After much discussion rosemary oil was suggested to try and cure this problem, the speed damage that had left my client with an oversensitive response to his environment.

A deep breath of rosemary oil while saying, "Healing the speed damage", on the inhalation had a very profound effect on my client's startle response and began healing his hypersensitivity very quickly indeed.

Much more research needs to be done in this area but I offer this story here simply as something to try if you feel this may apply to you.

Adrenaline Stop

Someone once told me that as soon as you relax then adrenaline ceases to be pumped around your body in less than 3 minutes! So that is even more reason to tap as soon as you start feeling anxious. Your system will be soothed and in no time the adrenaline levels in your body will be reduced and all will be well.

If you own an ipod or mp3 player 3 minutes is just one track! So make sure you have that with you with your favourite song ready to start playing and by the time it has finished your adrenaline levels will be back to normal.

And talking of hormones, smiling releases endorphins, the feel good hormones, it's something to do with movement of the muscles either side of the mouth. Smiling is also anchored to good times so a smile can trigger good memories.

So even though you may not feel like it, try smiling as soon as you feel anxious, it may feel a bit forced the first few times but it really does make a big difference which is why it's included in my Be Calm Now Checklist at the back of this book. ☺

Update

So, I've now completed my book on panic attacks and anxiety and for anyone who knows me they will understand what an enormous achievement this is for me.

Throughout writing it I have been very aware of revisiting old places and at times it has not been comfortable and I have discovered along the way that I did not clear some of the old feelings and fears. These are the ones that resurfaced though in a very definite way helped me to complete the project.

As a final step I took a trip to Paris. I went on a train through the Channel Tunnel, I stood in front of the Eiffel Tower and spent several glorious hours exploring the Left Bank, and came to realize that I have not lost my sensitivity or my ability to be absorbed, delighted, elated by my surroundings but to be totally aware of it all. The only thing I have lost is the freak out.

EFT does not take away your emotions, they stay, they will always be there, what you lose is the rubbish, that which makes life miserable.

I was always scared I would lose control and get overwhelmed but more than that I didn't want to be numb, I wanted to continue to feel everything and I fought for that tooth and nail and completely achieved it using EFT.

The difference between using desire and emotional states in goal setting and how they work, or not work, at all lies in the difference between WANT and NEED.

I started wanting to go away instead of needing to prove myself and this shifted my experiences exponentially.

The thing is, having learned the skills to rid myself of panic attacks I then went on to use them to enhance all my experiences. A couple of trips to Cuba plus a, completely out of character, journey to the Arctic Circle illustrated this beautifully so I have included here two reports to encourage and inspire you.

Dolphins Have Teeth!

EFT for the Traumas but EmoTrance for the Good Stuff

On a glorious holiday in Cuba, to celebrate my 50th birthday, I saw a notice for an excursion to swim with dolphins. Now I don't normally go in for that sort of thing, being in a posh 'holiday camp' type resort was pushing it a bit for me as it was, but, having spent five glorious days in Havana, and missing it terribly, it seemed a suitable diversion from the tedium of a sun drenched tropical beach and endless clear blue waves!

The tickets were booked but the day we were due to go I woke up feeling very uneasy and a little off colour. I soon realized I was scared of the idea of getting into the water with dolphins. After all, they are big, unpredictable, they have lots of very sharp teeth and they kill sharks for goodness sake!

So, though my fears seemed quite reasonable, I set about tapping that fear away as I really wanted to go.

- **Even though I am scared of swimming with dolphins...**

started at 10 and just would not shift, however hard I tapped or however many rounds I did.

Time was getting on and we were due to go and I paced our room up and down trying to work out why it just wasn't moving even though I was terrified, aha! terrified, and there I had it, two rounds of

- **Even though I am terrified of swimming with dolphins...**

got it down to zero in no time at all.

I just laughed and couldn't believe I hadn't spotted it sooner, I teach this stuff and had ignored the most basic of instructions, be precise! Just shows you what stress thinking does, completely scrambles your head/mind/thinking. Looking back I should have done an adrenaline tap there and then to clear my mind, give me some clarity as to why it wasn't working.

As it turned out our trip that day had to be cancelled which, even though I had dealt with my fear, I was relieved about as I was still feeling a little delicate. However, the next day, when we were scheduled to go, I didn't even think about it and was really quite excited and couldn't wait to leave.

The next hurdle was the slimy steps, covered with what looked like revolting pond scum, to get down to the platform and into the water. I'd eyed them with suspicion as the facilitator was telling us dos and don'ts before we entered the water and thought that may be the thing that prevents me from doing this. I hate slime, cannot eat slimy food or have anything to do with it and had never thought of treating it before but now seemed the perfect time. A discreet round of

- **Even though slime is disgusting...**

soon sorted it out. I can even eat cucumber now which had been off my list because of its slimy texture.

As I lowered myself into the water I felt an overwhelming sense of joy which I noticed could quite easily have heralded a panic attack in the past, energy just zoomed around me and I just used EmoTrance and let it channel out, it left from just below the base of my throat. This allowed an incoming of energy from the dolphins themselves and what a beautiful energy it is, loving, playful, I thought I may have been imagining it, anthropomorphizing these creatures from all I had heard but it was real enough. They definitely sensed those among us who needed a more gentle touch.

I was in awe of their power combined with their gentleness. They swam so close and you could feel the movement of their bodies, the feel of their tails, as they breezed past. And when they 'spoke' I could feel their vibrations throughout my body.

As I swam slowly I could feel their light touch, feel them swimming under me, round me, circling and creating a vortex, a downward pull, the feeling of old woes being sucked downwards and away.

As each dolphin came close our energy systems briefly entwined, for an instant being one, then gone again, the sensation so strong, almost deliberate, and very clearing, EmoTrancing the energy of each dolphin, always in at the heart but leaving in different places which felt like each dolphin had something different to share with me.

Twenty minutes later I was euphoric and wondering how much more I could take of this but soon realised I was not holding on to anything, there could be no 'explosion', the energies were being EmoTranced through, I was literally sucking them in but not holding on, letting each pass through, getting the last drop of goodness out of each vibration, but of course it had to end eventually!

When I left the dolphins, saying goodbye and thanking them, I felt reborn, strong and brave, ready to face new challenges in an altogether different way. A most amazing, enriching experience, as if new channels have been opened in me ready for something altogether bright and new to come into my life.

Bring it on, I'm ready!

EmoTrance and My Arctic Adventure

I've just been on the most extraordinary journey to the Arctic Circle with my mother and my faithful friend EmoTrance which, once again, didn't let me down!

The ship was late sailing so there was plenty of opportunity to use EmoTrance on my exasperation and exhaustion while wandering around Bergen and happening upon groups of desolate boat people also waiting, waiting for news of the boat's current position.

I just let each feeling soften and flow, whether it was a cramp in my shoulder from carrying my heavy bag around all day since early morning, or a feeling of annoyance that they were keeping us waiting so long. It all flowed out and I was able to keep my spirits up when all about me were losing it, big time.

We finally set sail at 4.30am and I was woken a couple of hours later being hurled out of my bunk with papers and books falling on my head from the shelf above. I righted myself just in time to catch a bottle of brandy that was sliding off the desktop. I stood for a while swaying with the movement and thought, right, this can either be a disaster or a triumph, it's up to me.

And immediately Energy Dancing sprang to mind, the way I found my body moving in unusual ways as I did when I was dancing. I let the energy flow and felt a rhythm building that I then found easy to follow to stay upright.

I quickly got dressed and set off to explore the ship. It was beautiful in the early dawn, deserted, with shadows of islands sailing by.

Breakfast was a challenge with a hundred or so people trying to balance plates of food and cups of scalding coffee as they made their way to their tables. By then I had found my feet and was following the sway of the boat. I was still dancing.

By lunchtime the storm out at sea was raging, with 20 metre waves and 55mph winds, and the captain steered the boat into a small port to sit it out in safety. We stayed for 8 hours.

Most of the route took us quite close to shore, protected by a chain of small islands but we needed to go out into the open sea for the next stretch, around a particularly treacherous point, notoriously dangerous even in relatively calm seas.

This he decided to do just after dinner when the waves had dropped to about 7 metres. It was going to be rough and we were told to finish dinner quickly then find somewhere to sit down for about an hour.

I could feel excitement welling up in me as I sat looking out over a blackness filled with foaming waves and catching glimpses of lights that disappeared for minutes at a time as the waves swelled up and dropped.

And something I had heard Bruce Springsteen say came to mind when he was asked if he ever got nervous before going out on stage.

He said, no, never, and went on to describe all the feelings he had which you and I would connect with being nervous, heart palpitations, dry mouth, sweating palms, which he took to be the sign that he was hyped up and ready to perform and that the more he had of these feelings the better he knew that his performance would be. Brilliant!

So that's how I let all those feelings go, the more intense the energy I felt swirling inside me the more I knew I was having fun and enjoying the experience. The energy flowed out of my hands and the top of my head until I was tingling all over with the energised end state.

It had worked like a dream and I really did enjoy the turbulent hour which I later found out had been filled with screaming desperate people clinging on for dear life with white knuckles and chucking up all over the place. I almost felt guilty I had enjoyed the experience so much. Almost :)

Now before this trip I just didn't do cold, in no way, shape or form, nada, nothing, no thank you. But it was extraordinary, ok, so I had all the arctic gear, that was only sensible, but even so, to stand on the top deck in a minus 22 degree arctic wind was, I feel, an achievement.

And not only that but to transcend those feelings of cold and just be able to suck in the glorious passing snow-capped landscape was a miracle.

The last evening during dinner an announcement was made that the Northern Lights could be seen off the starboard side. I have never run up four flights of stairs quite so quickly to the outside deck and then stood for a full five minutes, or maybe longer, without a coat, watching the most beautiful sight I have ever seen.

A magnificent streak of palest green swept across the night sky finishing with a small flourish. It took my breath away. It was only when someone came and put a blanket around my shoulders I realized just how cold it was out there, and dangerous, so I went inside to tog up and came back out and spent the next three hours marvelling at the spectacle long after others had gone inside.

The Lights were by no means strong, but they were there, that was what I had come to see and I was thrilled.

I found that forcing my eyes to see only made them fainter so I sat back inside myself and let them come to me and I was rewarded by huge intense flashes that lit up whole sides of mountains and rosy pink glows that nestled between some peaks.

I EmoTranced each one, really let the energy in, through and out and one particularly beautiful one, a fan shape over the startlingly crisp constellation of Orion triggered some amazing sounds inside me as the energy moved through me, like plucking different strings of a harp.

I found it difficult to drag myself away but by 1.30am I didn't feel it safe to stay out on an icy deck on my own so reluctantly went in to warm up and go to bed though sleep was slow in coming, I was so hyped up, so energized, felt so thankful I had been able to witness such an event. I finally drifted off in the early hours, breathing in sleep and breathing out the exhaustion and had the most intense dreams of strange lands, waking refreshed a few hours later and ready for the long journey home.

I managed to jump over all my reversals, and there were many, to take that trip, and I am so glad I did and feel so proud of myself for doing so!

Well done me and well done EmoTrance for making it such a memorable adventure.

Forward To The New!

This is just the beginning of your journey into the big wide world outside, it doesn't happen magically overnight, but then if it did it wouldn't be worth it.

You can join my Anxiety Help Newsgroup for continuing support and help from me and some friends who know what you have been through, and also to share your experiences.

You CAN do this, remember what I said at the beginning, 'If I can do this anyone can' and I wasn't kidding!

Best wishes on your truly adventurous journey,

Nicola

22 July 2008

Addenda

Guidance for Therapists

Therapists please note that what you will be dealing with mostly is the fear of fear.

A lot of people who consider themselves victims of constant panic attacks have only had one episode then live in constant fear of having another.

A panic attack is so terrifying that even the thought of having one can trigger all the symptoms, sweating, dizziness, confusion, palpitations, urgent need to go to the toilet, feelings of terror and needing to run and get away though often feeling too weak to move.

Your client will insist that he or she is not doing or thinking anything in particular when the panic attacks flash, as if they come from out of nowhere, and that it is the feelings of the attack that launch them into bad thoughts but this is not the case, and there are no exceptions to this. A panic attack ALWAYS starts with a bad thought, however quick, fleeting, or unnoticed.

It is your job to illicit exact opening statements to help them overcome the fear of the feelings and get this down to zero. Once the fear of the feelings has gone there will be no initial thought to trigger an attack.

There is an interesting phenomenon in EmoTrance called "Cascades". This happens when you start recalling a bunch of related memories and EmoTrancing them.

Say your client is having problems with guilt and starts to think of several incidences to EmoTrance. At first every memory seems like an effort but if you can encourage them to keep the momentum up, and have each one accessed in quick succession, soon a Cascade occurs and in the end they just flow, often without being able to see any pictures. All you need to do at this point is to encourage them, "You're doing really nicely, just keep them flowing".

This is an extremely valuable technique which can literally shave weeks, months and even years off therapy time so watch out for opportunities to initiate this powerful process.

How To Help A Loved One Who Suffers From Anxiety & Panic Attacks

by Silvia Hartmann

Imagine the scene. A rooftop, night, cold, windy.

At the edge of the roof stands a young lady, completely distraught and ready to jump.

She is tearing her hair, rocking, muttering insanely, crying, sometimes screaming random abuse and pain.

You walk up and what do you do now?

Now imagine, this young lady was your sister, your lover, your wife, your daughter, or your best friend.

Notice how immediately, the situation changes.

How now, YOU ARE AFRAID.

How now, you no longer know what to do and if you say the wrong thing, she WILL jump.

And here, in a nutshell, we have the problem that faces a person who loves someone who suffers from anxiety or panic attacks.

Fear breeds more fear.

Uncertainty breeds more uncertainty.

What a stressed person needs in another is a LOCUS of strength, clarity, and most of all, that FOCUS that they themselves now no longer have.

They need to be CALLED BACK to their normal mode of sane and resourceful functioning, like an aircraft in a fog needs the tower control to talk them down, every step of the way, until they have safely landed, exited, and have safe and supportive ground under their feet once more.

This is the job of anyone at all who wants to help a person in diSTRESS, whether they are in pain, having a psychotic attack, a drug experience gone wrong or a panic attack, it matters not.

When an ambulance crew arrives and faces a screaming person, bleeding and obviously "out of their mind" with distress, or with stress, we might as well call it, they will be calm and absolutely steady.
They will follow a set rule of procedures that they have learned during their training which keeps themselves focussed and the person in stress safe.

This is very much the same idea we will be following here; and like the ambulance crew, if you follow these procedures and become practised at using them, you too will be safe and EXTREMELY HELPFUL to have around in a moment of crisis.

YOUR Fear

At the core of all of this lies your own fear.

When a person becomes very distressed, and their behaviours and all their thoughts, all their feelings and their logic simply disappears in a whirlpool of adrenaline induced chaos, they trigger in anyone else who is around quite naturally all their own fears immediately - the other person becomes stressed as well.

But now, instead of one stressed person, we have two, and these will engage and enter a feedback loop of stress that frightens both.

The adrenaline induced chaos of thought, emotion and behaviour in stress needs above all else, a safety anchor in the storm, a light at the end of the tunnel, a steady guiding hand to bring them back to themselves and that is why YOU must be FEARLESS when you want to help others who are stressed.

This is just the same system for simply coping with everyday tantrums of children or co-workers as it is with high end situations like the young lady on the top of the roof.

So first of all, we need to deal with ALL YOUR FEARS about the situation, using the classic EFT protocol.

Although each is slightly different, there are some constants that come up again and again.

You can tap these opening statements first and then make a list of your own, one that covers all and every reservation you have about being perfectly able to STABILISE your loved one in a moment of crisis as well as, or much better still, than any professional armed with an injection needle.

1. Fear of Insanity

In our societies, there is a truly tremendous fear of insanity, culturally built in and culturally constantly re-inforced, probably to cement a tiny range of "acceptable" emotions and behaviours for control purposes.

In many people, fear of insanity is far, far higher and more insidious than fear of death, for example; this is rarely treated properly or even addressed at all in standard psychology and so even someone who has been in classical treatment for many years might have never even known they suffer from this problem.

Especially intelligent and highly creative people, with their unusual thoughts and internal representations, will be terrified of the "Nietzsche Effect" - "we all know" that genius and insanity go hand in hand, right?

Fear of insanity is one of the core reasons why people with anxiety attacks and their loved ones enter major stress loops, and to understand that behaviour under stress IS GOING TO BE

INSANE, because it can't be anything else, quite naturally and structurally, is a big step forward.

Opening Statements:

- **Even though I am terrified of (Susan's) insanity, I deeply and profoundly love and accept myself.**

Variation:

- **Even though I am terrified of (Susan's) insanity, I deeply and profoundly love and accept (Susan).**

Tap them both and tap these statements thoroughly, and until you really have them down to 0.

You might find as you tap these statements that more specific fears emerge, which will make your own personalised opening statements, such as:

- **Even though I am terrified (Susan) might hurt herself...**
- **Even though I am terrified (Susan) might die...**
- **Even though I am terrified (Susan) might harm me...**
- **Even though I am terrified (Susan) might leave me...**
- **Even though I am terrified (Susan) might be taken away from me...**
- **Even though I am terrified (Susan) might get worse because of me...**

Please be BRUTALLY HONEST with yourself when you do these opening statements. I chose the word "terrified", not just afraid, or uncomfortable, or worried. To watch someone really lose it and stand there and be stressed and helpless is really TERRIFYING as an experience; further, no-one need ever know just what you tapped on to make YOUR OWN PERSONAL BREAKTHROUGH on this topic.

2. YOUR Traumatic Memories

If you live with a person who suffers from severe anxiety or has panic attacks, then there will have been moments of high trauma - terrifying moments, like the lady on the roof, that become real, proper traumas for you. These are in structure no different at all to the sort of things that cause soldiers in a war to develop all kinds of fears, symptoms and post traumatic stress disorder.

As an example, one lady came home from work one day and found her husband lying on the bathroom floor, covered in blood, because he had cut his wrists.

This picture was "burned into her mind" and it was so terrifying to her that she just couldn't cope with it at all and HAD to leave him; the thought of this moment was with her every time she left the flat and regardless of whether he was particularly stressed at the time.

Before she left him, the last few weeks were a nightmare for her because she lived now herself in a constant state of high anxiety and didn't dare speak to him or do anything at all in case she might say the wrong thing, do the wrong thing, and he would "freak out" again.

This is the polar opposite to the calm and supportive ambulance crew of course, or the focussed, compassionate tower control operator talking the frightened pilot down.

However, because of HER TRAUMA, we can't possibly expect her to function properly herself now; SHE NEEDED HELP just as badly as her husband did.

So, if this story has reminded you of any number of incidents that are "burned into your mind" like that, and they don't have to be so dramatic as this example, then we need to clear them now - just for you, and regardless of whatever may become of any relationships further down the line.

Here are some examples of how to deal with such incidents.

In general, and rather than using a single opening statement, you simply tell the story of how you remember the incident WHILST YOU TAP.

You will find that there are very specific moments which ENCAPSULATE the trauma of the event.

In our example, they went like this:

- "I went into the bathroom and there was **all this blood**..."

Clearly, the image of "all this blood" was what was "burned into her mind" and tapping on simply just "All this blood..." produced major releases and shifts in the very first round.

But keep tapping until you really do "heave a sigh of relief" and you know the trauma is gone from that moment, from that image of the past.

In the example, the words went on as follows,

with the important parts which were tapped highlighted:

- **"I stood as frozen and my heart stood still."**
- **"I knew I had failed him totally, I had failed totally."**
- **"I should have known there was something wrong."**

The final opening statement in this example, and the one that produced the greatest result in changing this ladies mind about herself and the incident was this:

- **"I can't help anyone I love, I'm not good enough, not strong enough."**

Once the lady had tapped this statement, the old trauma collapsed completely and she came out of it knowing that she was indeed, a powerful and competent human being who COULD make a big difference and help other people - AND HERSELF.

3. Understanding The Effects Of Stress & Anxiety

A person who is reeling drunk is NOT held responsible for their actions by a court of law - because they really didn't know what they were doing, because their CAPACITY for clear and logical thought had disappeared, because they really no longer knew right from wrong.

People who are "tanked up on adrenaline" are in exactly the same position.

They do NOT know what they are doing, they don't know what they are saying, and they don't know right from wrong anymore either.

For someone who is on the outside of this, who LIVES with an alcoholic or a stressed out person, or a drug addict, it is of the essence to understand that the REAL PERSON IS NOT PRESENT UNDER THE INFLUENCE of adrenaline.

They are NOT thinking straight, and whatever random nonsense they come up with during those times is exactly and ONLY that - random nonsense that isn't worth the paper it isn't printed on.

Whether they are shouting about demonic voices, the CIA bugging the electrical outlets, horrors and pains of the past, how they are going to die this very moment because they can't go on, this is all the equivalent of "pill talk" - please DO NOT TAKE ANY OF IT SERIOUSLY OR EVEN IN AT ALL.

In other words, to try and "talk someone out of it" with reasoned argument is an entirely pointless exercise and likely to make the disturbances in their systems worse, because you're feeding the same nonsense that is the RESULT of their disturbed output right back into the system.

The simple rule is that the more stressed a person becomes, the more bizarre and illogical their reasoning and their talking becomes too and at the same time.

This is completely systemic and holds not just for your stressed loved one, but for me, and for you, and for the President of the United States just as well.

Stressed people say very hurtful and untrue things about themselves, about life, about you - and none of it is worth a dime. It's just "stress talk". They really DON'T mean a word of it, because they can't.

For us, out on the other side, who hear these frightening, hurtful, insane and awful things, it can be quite difficult to keep a calm energy system and realise that a stress loop of insanity is about to develop, and if we go on playing that particular game, we will both end up saying and doing all kinds of things that are highly unproductive in every sense of the word.

The reason I'm mentioning this is that unless you know this, you or your loved one might have taken a great many things "seriously" and "to heart" which were nothing but random stress talk and utterly meaningless, and worthless.

Have a think what decisions or beliefs you have made from this stress talk/stress behaviour that are now getting in everyone's way.

Here are some examples:

- **"Even though Susan thinks she's worthless, I deeply and profoundly love and accept Susan."**
- **"Even though Susan thinks I'm useless..."**
- **"Even though I think Susan is just a coward..."**
- **"Even though Susan thinks it's all over..."**
- **"Even though I think she'll never live a normal life..."**
- **"Even though Susan thinks I don't really love her..."**

There are as many variations on this theme as there are individuals involved; you will know the ones that are always coming up when stress rears its ugly head and logic, friendliness, compassion and joy go out of the window.

The truth at the end of the day is that you are BOTH fine, very resourceful individuals with immense value, so much there waiting to unfold itself. That's the only truth IN REALITY and in real truth, and if you really get to work at the issues that stand between either of you and THAT TRUTH, changes will happen for the better, and very quickly, at that.

First Aid Procedures

The first of our first aid procedures is not about your loved one, but about YOU.

1. Be CALM & Steady

Are you stressed now?

If so, stop and take a deep breath.

Leave the room and tap yourself if you have to, or walk away and TREAT YOURSELF.

If you are stressed, you'll be no good to anyone, including your loved one.

This is akin to the instruction given on airplanes about mothers having to put the oxygen mask on their own faces FIRST, and only then, put the second oxygen mask on the baby.

If they try to do it the other way around, BOTH MOTHER AND BABY WILL DIE.

Remember also that if you are stressed you will make WRONG DECISIONS and say and do the WRONG things.

So YOU need to get aware of YOUR OWN stress levels and when they get to a point where logic and sanity is being threatened, you need to take a time out and centre yourself, firstly and foremostly.

NB. If you have treated yourself for Points 1-3 above, you will already be markedly calmer and more COMPETENT than you ever used to be; this step is going to be much easier than you ever thought possible.

2. Reduce Stress

Movement is one of the best stress reducers and most natural one. If you can get the person to move, perhaps move away from a situation, stimulus, or walk with you, a great many full panic or anxiety attacks never come into being in the first place.

Also remember movement as a general stress reducer in every day life. We are built for fight or flight responses to adrenaline being present in our systems, and panic attacks often happen when a person feels "stuck" and incapable of moving away from something that is frightening them. If you know of NLP, you know that one can even "turn one's back" on an idea, or walk away from a thought, quite literally.

The same goes for you too, of course. TVs can be switched off, pictures turned face down, letters put away into a drawer and many other stressful stimuli removed using that kind of movement; we can get back to them later when we are more centred.

Please note that often very stressed people might fight this "movement away from" what frightens them because they are thinking illogically that it is some form of defeat, rather than the sensible thing to do at the time.

3. Direct, Focused Instructions

Under stress, not just the field of vision collapses into "tunnel vision" but also the range of thought, into "tunnel thinking". Emotions collapse into "tunnel feelings" and then the nasty spider, thought or heartache becomes a literal hell and is "all there is".

Thus, a stressed person can claim wholeheartedly that "nobody loves me" when their entire family and a hundred thousand well meaning fans are clustered in deep rows right around their bedside.

All the resources of intelligence, foresight, creativity, intuition, courage, strength, experience and so on and so on are then OUTSIDE of that "tunnel vision" - to the stressed person it is then in actuality as though these didn't even exist at all.

What gets through and has a chance to get "into that tunnel thinking" are CLEAR, DIRECT INSTRUCTIONS.

"Put that gun down. Put it down. Put that gun down, now. Put it down. Put the gun down." Calmly, repeated many times, simple, clear instructions like this are given to stressed people and they are heard eventually. They get through.

Depending on your situation, and with you being clear and focussed, you can find such a clear instruction, even if is, "Take a step back. Take just one step back, step back. Step back. Take a step back."

The mind of the stressed person can focus on this, and this instruction becomes a lifeline in their internal storm. Any smallest indication that it is being heard, being received, being PROCESSED, such as a flickering of the lids, a quick downward look at the feet, a beginning of a movement to complete that instruction is then re-inforced calmly, praised calmly, and all you need to say then is, "Very good. You are doing very, very well. Take a step back, that's very good, well done ..."

Now, I understand that some might think that this is a very "unnatural" way to address Susan (my wife, my mother, my daughter, my lover...) but we must remember that Susan as such isn't really here at the moment. She is lost in a storm and these repetitive words and most basic, most simple of encouragements are giving the REAL Susan a lifeline to come out and take charge herself again as is right and proper. When Susan is REALLY back (and you know what that is like!), THEN we can have a meaningful conversation, and not before.

If your partner/loved one knows how to do EFT themselves, or even if they don't, a very beneficial instruction is: "Tap under your eye. Just tap under your eye..."

The added benefit of the meridian energy balancing will bring them "out" of the storm much, much more quickly than other simple random behaviour sequences ever could by themselves. This is very useful and brings me to the one last major first aid technique, namely:

4. Breathing

"Take a breath, just breathe. Take a deep breath, take a deep breath in, that's very, very good! You're doing really well. Breathe, just breathe..."

That instruction is completely hypnotic and immensely helpful. It is a version of "movement" and helps reduce adrenaline quickly. Remember this instruction also for yourself. It is truly in many situations an absolute life saver and can really prevent us from making possibly fatal mistakes.

NB: If a person is breathing shallow and way too fast (technical term - hyperventilating), get them breathing into a bag of any kind, or even into a pillow. But the instructions, slow and rhythmical to take a deep, slow breath stay essentially the same.

5. Food & Drink

Insulin decreases adrenaline, but also the act of accepting and handling "a nice cup of hot tea" or even a mint is the movement/instruction double we have already talked about before. Many people get addicted to alcohol because it is often habitual in our society to use "a stiff drink" for this purpose and then the relaxation that occurs is falsely tied into the alcohol - which then becomes a stress device.

Getting a stressed person to eat or drink is the final way to get them out of a building stress loop and back into equilibrium. Smokers use cigarettes for the same reason.

Long Term Focus

To conclude, I would like to state one more time how immensely important it is to remain calm yourself, and to take care of YOURSELF first and foremost.

Remember the mothers and babies with their oxygen masks.

You KNOW what a wonderful human being your loved one is and just how much immense potential to have to really shine when they are their own true selves, and not in a state of hysterics and "tunnel thinking".

That is the "true Susan" if you will, and that's where we have to keep our focus completely.

Susan, our symbolic loved one here, is NOT the stress creature.

Susan really IS strong, and powerful, and beautiful, and the less stress she has, and the clearer she becomes, the more often she will be herself as she truly is.

WE can help HER the best by focussing on that, tapping our own doubts about ourselves and about "her" and clearing OURSELVES of stress, past traumas and limiting decisions.

EFT is truly the perfect tool for this, because it is so easy to use, and so quick; it brings good results right away and you can do it as soon as you have discovered something that gets in your way of being calm and centred yourself first of all.

When YOU ARE, then you become a whole new resource for "Susan" too.

The stronger YOU become, the more strength your loved one can draw from you and use this to repair themselves.

And that's the last point I would really like to stress.

YOU cannot "heal" your loved one.

They have to do that for themselves, in their own time.

But if they have a true CHAMPION in you, someone who really believes in them, who knows just how wonderful they are and keeps that steady, burning brightly and in full focus, they will be amongst the luckiest and fewest people on this Earth.

All my best wishes to you, and to your loved one,

Silvia
Silvia Hartmann
December 2004

Acknowledgment and Thanks

To Silvia Hartmann for her considerable material support, friendship and encouragement and without whom this book would not have been written.

http://SilviaHartmann.com

Further Reading

Adventures in EFT
by Silvia Hartmann
I cannot recommend this book highly enough. It is THE definitive work on EFT and lists many hundreds of applications for this amazing technique to treat a wide variety of problems. It is practical and packed with information and helpful tips and is the bestselling guide for beginners in Gary Craig's Emotional Freedom Techniques (EFT).

The Advanced Patterns of EFT
by Silvia Hartmann
For those who wish to investigate further this is an excellent book with dozens of new patterns and techniques to play with.

Oceans Of Energy – The Techniques and Patterns of EmoTrance Vol. 1
by Silvia Hartmann
I love EmoTrance and I love this book and not just because I co-developed the technique! I use

EmoTrance daily and this book explains clearly how to use this simple, brand new healing modality which extends far beyond cessation of pain and into nourishing yourself from the world around you. An absolute essential.

Living Energy – The Techniques and Patterns of EmoTrance Vol. 2
by Silvia Hartmann
More amazing techniques and patterns covering the wider energy body, the Jelly Bean Pattern is worth the cost of the book alone and is how I found my wonderful beachside home within ten days of doing it!

Project Sanctuary
by Silvia Hartmann
I use Project Sanctuary daily, not just as a personal growth tool but as a quiet place to go and be calm, sort out problems, develop my creativity and just listen to my heart.

**The Genius Symbols
by Silvia Hartmann**

The Genius Symbols were created as a way of opening a two way communication with the unconscious mind, the energy mind, and I find them invaluable for all kinds of problem solving and ways to find creative solutions, big and small, that really work in every day life. Well worth investigating.

**Aromatherapy For Your Soul
By Silvia Hartmann**

This totally new concept of what essential oils are and how to find out which one is right for you is groundbreaking and a treat not to be missed. There are 121 beautiful stories to help you find the oil you need right now and almost as many innovative ways to use them.

Visit http://Dragonrising.com for a huge selection of personal development books, online courses, CDs and free downloads including meditation MP3s and demo versions of products.

All Books and CDs available from:

DragonRising Publishing
45 Gildredge Road
Eastbourne BN21 4RY
United Kingdom

Tel: +44 (0)1323 700 123
Web: http://DragonRising.com

About Nicola Quinn

Nicola Quinn is an Author, experienced international AMT Trainer, Sidereus Energy Healer, Reiki Master, Environmental Energy Consultant and a Homoeopathic and Nutritional Consultant with a particular focus on women's health issues.

She is a Director of The Association for Meridian and Energy Therapies, a Director of The StarFields Network, and co-founded The Sidereus Foundation and co-developed EmoTrance with Dr. Silvia Hartmann and has worked closely with her for a number of years researching human energy fields.

Nicola Quinn's specialist areas are anxiety and panic attacks and family energy fields and her ability to accurately identify and correct vibrational insufficiencies is world renowned.

Nicola is an abstract artist and has exhibited locally in her home town in East Sussex, UK.

She is also a classically trained musician and composes pieces to create certain states, and as inspiration, for specific paintings and projects. Her first album, Star Music, has already received very favourable reviews.

Books and Papers

- Alternative Pain Relief (2008)
- Life Without Panic Attacks (2005)
- The Easy Grape Cure (2003)
- The MET Chakra Protocol (2002)
- Tachyon EmoTrance Self Healing (with Dr. Silvia Hartmann) (2002)
- Bob Beck Protocol (Editor) (2000)

Recordings

- Star Music (2008)
- EmoTrance Experience Day Live Recording (2006)

Trainings and Presentations

- Project Sanctuary Masters
- EmoTrance Practitioner
- Advanced EmoTrance Practitioner
- MET Practitioner
- Advanced MET Practitioner
- Energy Healing for Animals
- The Story Teller
- Reiki I Practitioner
- Reiki II Practitioner
- Reiki Master

Visit http://NicolaQuinn.com for more information on energy healing techniques, energy products, health articles, free downloads, meditation mp3s, custom remedies and telephone consultations.

Be Calm Now Checklist

1. Stop!
2. Take a deep breath, from your abdomen, saying on the inbreath, "I am calm and relaxed".
3. Tap or rub your emergency stop point, while continuing to breath deeply. Or use the Calming Points, UE, UA, CB.
4. This is not a catastrophe and will pass!
5. Smell your oil, "I am calm and relaxed" as you breath in deeply.
6. Well done, your system is already calming with each breath and adrenaline is already dispersing.
7. Smile! Get those endorphins working for you ☺
8. Forgive yourself for feeling scared.
9. You're doing brilliantly and remember it's ok to feel strange in a strange situation!

You are a strong, powerful, capable person and I am so proud of you.

Congratulations!